RK
X

54.  MOROCCO _____

55.  SIAM _____

---

**Write one of the given words in each of the sentences.**

council,   counsel,   counsellor,   councillo

56.  He lost his passport on holiday and went to see the British _____ for help.

57.  The _____ did her very best to persuade the couple to try to make their marriage work.

58.  The borough _____ decided to improve the lighting on the main road.

59.  "I must _____ you to tell the truth," the judge told the prisoner in the dock.

60.  We asked our local _____ if she would support our campaign for new play equipment in the park.

---

**The prefix 'bene-' means 'good' or 'well'. Complete these sentences.**

61.  A person who helps by providing money is a  bene _ _ _ _ _ _ _ .

62.  Something which is good for you is   bene _ _ _ _ _ _ _ .

63.  Someone kindly or generous is   bene _ _ _ _ _ _ _ .

64.  If you receive money from a will you are a  bene _ _ _ _ _ _ _ _ .

65.  A blessing at the end of a church service is a bene _ _ _ _ _ _ _ .

---

**Fill in the missing words.**

66.  A young tree is called a _____ .

67.  A tin in which tea is kept is called a _____ .

68.  People watching a sport are the _____ .

69.  Leather is cured in a _____ .

70.  A period of ten years is a _____ .

---

**The names of the parliaments of these five countries are given. Write each parliament next to its country.**

Knesset,   Althing,   Congress,   Dáil,   Cortes

71.  ICELAND _____

72.  EIRE _____

73.  SPAIN _____

74.  ISRAEL _____

75.  USA _____

---

**Complete these proverbs.**

76.  A nod is as good as a wink _____ .

77.  Beggars cannot _____ .

78.  Let bygones _____ .

MARK
✓ or ✗

| | | | |
|---|---|---|---|
| Complete these proverbs. | 79. | You cannot make a silk purse _____ . | ☐ |
| | 80. | Marry in haste, _____ . | ☐ |

| | | | |
|---|---|---|---|
| Underline the ADJECTIVES in each sentence. | 81. | Three hungry children sat at the fourth table. | ☐ |
| | 82. | My young cousin is related to her sister. | ☐ |
| | 83. | There are a few new products in the shop each day. | ☐ |
| | 84. | Which pen did that unruly child break? | ☐ |
| | 85. | These fresh flowers will cheer up his poorly mother. | ☐ |

| | | | |
|---|---|---|---|
| Rewrite these sentences, changing them to reported speech. | 86. | "What time is the last bus?" asked Anthony. | ☐ |
| | 87. | "Can you tell me the way to the Town Hall?" the stranger asked me. | ☐ |
| | 88. | "Are these your gloves John?" asked Syrita. | ☐ |
| | 89. | "Can you spare a copper?" the tramp asked Stanley. | ☐ |
| | 90. | "Will you marry me Cinderella?" asked Prince Charming. | ☐ |

Put each of the given words in its correct sentence.

prized,   prised,   toed,   towed,   toad

| | | | |
|---|---|---|---|
| | 91. | He _____ the ball gently before passing it back to the goalkeeper. | ☐ |
| | 92. | Kate _____ off the lid and looked inside the box. | ☐ |
| | 93. | Sean's new bicycle was his _____ possession. | ☐ |
| | 94. | We saw a _____ by the mill pond. | ☐ |
| | 95. | The car had to be _____ to a garage for repair. | ☐ |

| | | | |
|---|---|---|---|
| Fill in the missing information in these sentences. | 96. | The Montgolfier brothers in 1783 made the first _____ in a _____ . | ☐ |
| | 97. | Sir Christopher Wren in 1675 began to build the new _____ , the original having been destroyed in 1666. | ☐ |
| | 98. | The first part of John Bunyan's book _____ was published in 1678. | ☐ |
| | 99. | Joseph Lister in 1865 introduced _____ into the operating theatre. | ☐ |
| | 100. | In the 1760s James Hargreaves introduced his _____ , allowing one person to spin several threads at the same time. | ☐ |

MARK
✓ or ✗

| | | |
|---|---|---|
| Write each of the given popular phrases next to its meaning. | | lead the life of Riley, not to be sneezed at, rooted to the spot, the sport of kings, a square peg in a round hole |
| | 1. | unable to move _____ ☐ |
| | 2. | someone not suited _____ ☐ |
| | 3. | live in great comfort _____ ☐ |
| | 4. | shouldn't be turned down _____ ☐ |
| | 5. | horse racing _____ ☐ |

| | | |
|---|---|---|
| Write the missing word in each sentence. | 6. | Someone who dies for a just or holy cause is a _____ . ☐ |
| | 7. | A coin issued on special occasions with a face value of 25 pence is called a _____ . ☐ |
| | 8. | A statue often stands on top of a _____ . ☐ |
| | 9. | The frame on which people were put to death by hanging was called the _____ . ☐ |
| | 10. | The room in which a scientist works is a _____ . ☐ |

| | | |
|---|---|---|
| Starting with the word 'Despite' and using a comma, join these pairs of sentences together. | 11. | The weather was appalling. He still went to school. _____ ☐ |
| | 12. | There were a lot of problems. The building was finished on time. _____ ☐ |
| | 13. | The child's behaviour was dreadful. The teacher was lenient. _____ ☐ |
| | 14. | Her leg was broken. She insisted on going to work. _____ ☐ |
| | 15. | He had a poor work-record. He still got the job. _____ ☐ |

| | | |
|---|---|---|
| Write the city and/or country where each of these is found. | 16. | The Eiffel Tower is in the city of _____ in _____ . ☐ |
| | 17. | The Golden Gate Bridge is near the city of _____ in the United _____ of _____ . ☐ |
| | 18. | If you were standing by the Sphinx you would be in the country of _____ . ☐ |
| | 19. | Table Mountain is in the country of S_____ A_____ . ☐ |
| | 20. | The Alhambra Palace is in Granada in the country of _____ . ☐ |

| | | |
|---|---|---|
| Underline the PRONOUNS in these sentences. | 21. | You and I ought to try and sort this out. ☐ |
| | 22. | "Is that book yours or mine?" she asked her mother. ☐ |

MARK
✓ or ✗

| Underline the PRONOUNS in these sentences. | 23. | I gave myself five minutes' rest. | ☐ |
| | 24. | We must look after ourselves. | ☐ |
| | 25. | Will you or she give the dog its dinner? | ☐ |

Put the given words into their correct sentences.

rode,   road,   rowed,   bark,   barque

26. The boss isn't really cross with you. Her _____ is worse than her bite. ☐

27. She _____ her bicycle for hundreds of kilometres. ☐

28. A _____ was a small sailing ship. ☐

29. He _____ across the lake in the leaking boat. ☐

30. Whichever _____ you take, you will get there on time. ☐

Write down the masculine and feminine of these creatures.

| GENUS | MASCULINE | FEMININE | |
|---|---|---|---|
| 31. HORSE | _____ | _____ | ☐ |
| 32. HARE | _____ | _____ | ☐ |
| 33. GOOSE | _____ | _____ | ☐ |
| 34. OX | _____ | _____ | ☐ |
| 35. SHEEP | _____ | _____ | ☐ |

Difficult spellings. Fill in the missing letters.

36. an advantage or a favour   p _ _ _ _ _ _ _ e ☐

37. a boat with sails   y _ _ _ _ ☐

38. the state of being husband and wife   m _ _ _ _ _ _ e ☐

39. yes, indeed   d _ _ _ _ _ _ _ _ y ☐

40. the second month   F _ _ _ _ _ _ _ ☐

Complete these proverbs.

41. One man's loss _____ ☐

42. All that glitters (or glistens) _____ ☐

43. It's six of one _____ ☐

44. Time and tide _____ ☐

45. It never rains _____ ☐

'Mal-' is a prefix which means 'bad'. Complete these sentences.

46. An illness or a disease is a   mal _ _ _ _ . ☐

47. Clumsy or unskilful is   mal _ _ _ _ _ _ _ . ☐

48. When something goes wrong it   mal _ _ _ _ _ _ _ _ s. ☐

49. A person who does wrong is a   mal _ _ _ _ _ _ _ _ . ☐

50. Someone who wishes evil on somebody else is
mal _ _ _ _ _ _ _ t. ☐

MARK
✓ or ✗

**Fill in these group terms.**

51.  a _____ of insects

52.  a _____ of chickens

53.  a _____ of dancers

54.  a _____ of ships

55.  A number of flowers in a bunch is a _____ .

---

**Underline the odd one out.**

56.  cassowary   owl   ostrich   emu   penguin

57.  servile   obsequious   sycophantic   uncivil   unctuous

58.  august   march   exalted   majestic   imperial

59.  aster   petunia   poplar   hyacinth   chrysanthemum

60.  Nelson   Drake   Churchill   Hawkins   Cook   Raleigh

---

**Supply the missing plurals.**

61.  A STRATUM is a layer or level and its plural is _____ .

62.  A DIE is a small cube with numbered faces, used in gambling or board games, and its plural is _____ .

63.  A RADIUS is the line from the centre of a circle to the circumference. Its plural is _____ or _____ .

64.  A GAZEBO is a belvedere, a place from which to admire the view. Its plural is either _____ or _____ .

65.  The word MONEY also has two plurals, either _____ or _____ .

---

**Write the correct capital city and currency from the list next to each of these five countries.**

Rabat, Pound, Pound, Pretoria, London, Dirham, Stockholm, Rand, Krona, Valletta

| COUNTRY | CAPITAL | CURRENCY |
| --- | --- | --- |
| 66. England | _____ | _____ |
| 67. Morocco | _____ | _____ |
| 68. Malta | _____ | _____ |
| 69. South Africa | _____ | _____ |
| 70. Sweden | _____ | _____ |

---

**Supply the missing information.**

71.  _____ and _____ Wright in 1903 were the first men in the world to fly a powered _____ .

72.  Joseph Priestley in 1774 discovered the gas called _____ .

73.  In 1476 William Caxton set up the first _____ in England.

MARK
✓ or ✗

| Supply the missing information. | 74. | Edmund Hillary and Tenzing Norgay in 1953 were the first men to set foot on the top of _____ . | ☐ |
| | 75. | The Rosetta stone, found in Egypt in 1799, enabled historians to understand ancient Egyptian _____ . | ☐ |

| Complete the similes using the given animals. | | lamb,   horse,   mouse,   lion,   bulldog | |
| | 76. | as brave as a _____ | ☐ |
| | 77. | as quiet as a _____ | ☐ |
| | 78. | as strong as a _____ | ☐ |
| | 79. | as tenacious as a _____ | ☐ |
| | 80. | as gentle as a _____ | ☐ |

| On each line write one word which has both the meanings given. | 81. | a fishing vessel _____ to slap loudly | ☐ |
| | 82. | a share _____ to hit hard | ☐ |
| | 83. | a narrow opening _____ to strike a blow | ☐ |
| | 84. | a hired horse _____ to kick the shins | ☐ |
| | 85. | a large bag _____ to plunder and ravage | ☐ |

| Rewrite correctly, putting in the necessary punctuation. | 86-90. | not only blacksmiths have anvils said shirley youve one in your ear _____ _____ _____ | Number between 0 and 5 ☐ |

| Write down the missing information. | 91. | The Doge was the leader in _____ . | ☐ |
| | 92. | A cairn is a pile of _____ often to show the way. | ☐ |
| | 93. | If you were a cartographer your job would be to make _____ . | ☐ |
| | 94. | A synopsis is a _____ . | ☐ |
| | 95. | A wyvern is a _____ . | ☐ |

| Unscramble these anagrams to match the meanings given in brackets. | 96. | RIVER ROSE (stored water) _____ | ☐ |
| | 97. | SIR LOOPY CHARM (two words, it is a place to learn) _____ | ☐ |
| | 98. | MESS THE VICAR (two words, meaning before a festival) _____ | ☐ |
| | 99. | RIB LIES (funny) _____ | ☐ |
| | 100. | TO BE DUD (wasn't sure) _____ | ☐ |

MARK
✓ or ✗

Write down the antonyms of these words, using a prefix.

1. audible _____

2. inflate _____

3. wind _____

4. efficient _____

5. literate _____

Complete these analogies.

6. Policeman is to thief as _____ is to poacher.

7. Methuselah is to age as Solomon is to _____ .

8. ABC is to Alpha, Bravo, Charlie, as DEF is to _____

_____  _____

9. Pearl is to _____ as diamond is to sixty.

10. Telephone is to Bell as _____ is to Marconi.

Rewrite, putting in the necessary punctuation.

11-15. oi shouted p c dodsworth what dyou think youre doing

_____

_____

_____

Number between 0 and 5

Put each of the given popular phrases next to its correct meaning.

wool-gathering,  out of the wood,  to drown one's sorrows,
to give up the ghost,  to pull through

16. to die _____

17. thinking of other things _____

18. to survive _____

19. to drink a lot in order to forget _____

20. free from difficulty _____

Write these five names in alphabetical order (the order in which they would appear in a telephone directory).

21. Michael Smith _____

22. Alfred Simmons _____

23. Anne Smyth _____

24. Anne Smythe _____

25. Paul Smithson _____

Briefly define these phrases.

26. cock-a-leekie _____

27. cock-and-bull story _____

28. cock-a-hoop _____

29. cock crow _____

30. cock-eyed _____

MARK
✓ or ✗

**Rewrite these sentences in the plural form.**

31. He declared that the duchess's tiara had been stolen.
   _____ ☐

32. The fisherman caught a trout and a plaice.
   _____ ☐

33. The thief took the knife from the loaf and put it on the shelf.
   _____
   _____ ☐

34. The army camped by the city in the valley.
   _____ ☐

35. The hero enjoyed playing a solo on the banjo, piano or piccolo.
   _____
   _____ ☐

**These counties are abbreviated. Write them out in full.**

36. Herts. _____ ☐
37. S. Yorks. _____ ☐
38. Glos. _____ ☐
39. Cambs. _____ ☐
40. Leics. _____ ☐

**Write down one word to describe all on each line.**

41. ball and socket, dovetail, mortise and tenon _____ ☐
42. Etna, Vesuvius, Krakatoa, Stromboli _____ ☐
43. apostrophe, colon, comma, inverted comma _____ ☐
44. aren't, sci-fi, gym, CID _____ ☐
45. Malta, Sardinia, Easter, St Helena _____ ☐

**In each sentence write a NOUN formed from the word in capitals.**

46. BANKRUPT    Because of her _____ she was
                penniless.                                ☐

47. TRAGIC      The fire was a _____ which left
                them homeless.                           ☐

48. COPIOUS     He was pleased with the _____
                of the harvest.                          ☐

49. OBSCURE     Most of today's celebrities will fade into
                _____ .                         ☐

50. ARID        Nothing grew in the bleak _____ of
                the desert.                              ☐

**Underline the word which is closest in meaning to the word in capitals.**

51. HEAVENLY      diabolical  celestial  pure  beautiful  sinless   ☐
52. OPPROBRIUM    disease  distress  irritation  brutality  censure ☐
53. HAVOC         devastation  denunciation  diversion  dilation  drama ☐
54. ANARCHY       figure  lawlessness  bishop  cookery  failure    ☐
55. LITHE         lumber  limbless  limbo  limber  limp            ☐

MARK
✓ or ✗

**Complete these sentences.**

56. A misogynist is a person who hates _____ .

57. The obverse of a British coin shows the _____ .

58. If someone is decapitated he gets his _____ .

59. A somnambulist _____ .

60. A mimic is a person who _____ .

**Underline the odd one out in each line.**

61. right   acute   obtuse   isosceles   reflex

62. slip   square leg   mid off   cover point   batsman

63. granny   nephew   bowline   clove   sheepshank

64. verbal   nasal   oral   vocal   spoken

65. dove   hawk   buzzard   falcon   kestrel

**'Sub-' is a prefix which means 'under'. Complete these sentences.**

66. Someone lower in rank is   sub _ _ _ _ _ _ _ _ .

67. Under the sea is   sub _ _ _ _ _ _ .

68. Under the earth is   sub _ _ _ _ _ _ _ _ _ .

69. A tunnel for foot passengers is a   sub _ _ _ .

70. To put under the surface is to   sub _ _ _ _ _ .

**Complete these proverbs.**

71. Nothing ventured, _____

72. A leopard cannot _____

73. Strike while _____

74. When in Rome, _____

75. If speech is silver, _____

**Put each word in its correct sentence.**

meat,   meet,   mete,   mean,   mien

76. I _____ to accomplish what I have set out to do.

77. Can you _____ me at two o'clock tomorrow?

78. Some people like to have a joint of _____ at the weekend.

79. With humble _____ he begged his victim's forgiveness.

80. Part of a judge's duty is to _____ out justice.

**Here are some unusual names for colours. Write down the colour of which each one is a shade, e.g. citron is a shade of yellow.**

81. Crimson is a shade of _____ .

82. Indigo is a shade of _____ .

83. Jet is a shade of _____ .

84. Cinnamon is a shade of _____ .

85. Emerald is a shade of _____ .

MARK
✓ or ✗

Rewrite these
sentences correctly.

86.  A second series of plays are being planned.

     _____  ☐

87.  The escaped herd of cows are ruining the wheat crop.

     _____  ☐

88.  A bouquet of flowers are just what Carol needs.

     _____  ☐

89.  The brigade of guards were marching through the town.

     _____  ☐

90.  The crew are in a state of mutiny.

     _____  ☐

Write one word for
each of these phrases.

91.  the practice of spying   e _ _ _ _ _ _ _ _   ☐
92.  not allowed by law   i _ _ _ _ _ _ _   ☐
93.  The sending of thoughts from one person's mind to another's is
     called   t _ _ _ _ _ _ _ _ _ .   ☐
94.  A large airship used in the First World War was a
     di _ i _ i _ _ _ .   ☐
95.  Melted rock from under the earth is known as   l _ _ _   or
     m _ _ _ _ .   ☐

Change these
sentences to direct
speech.

96.  Bill shouted for the ball to be passed to him.

     _____  ☐

97.  Pauline asked her Mum if dinner was ready.

     _____  ☐

98.  The hermit replied that he preferred to live alone.

     _____  ☐

99.  The magistrate asked the burglar if he could think of any good
     reason why he should not be sent to prison.

     _____

     _____  ☐

100. The felon replied that he had a wife and two small children to
     support and demanded to know who would look after them were
     he to be sent to jail.

     _____

     _____

     _____  ☐

MARK
✓ or ✗

| | | |
|---|---|---|
| Briefly explain each of these phrases. | 1. | down at heel _____ |
| | 2. | downcast _____ |
| | 3. | downfall _____ |
| | 4. | down payment _____ |
| | 5. | down-to-earth _____ |

| | | |
|---|---|---|
| Rewrite these sentences, putting in any necessary punctuation. | 6. | john asked where have you been _____ |
| | 7. | where have you been asked john _____ |
| | 8. | where asked john have you been _____ |
| | 9. | john asked where i had been _____ |
| | 10. | pardon i replied _____ |

| | | |
|---|---|---|
| Write down what these abbreviations mean. | 11. | BST _____ |
| | 12. | IOU _____ |
| | 13. | C. of E. _____ |
| | 14. | C-in-C _____ |
| | 15. | OT _____ |

| | | |
|---|---|---|
| Underline the odd one out in each line. | 16. | Minotaur   Medusa   cockatrice   Cyclops   Jacuzzi |
| | 17. | apiary   heronry   rookery   aviary   nest |
| | 18. | Victory   Rocket   Titanic   Mary Celeste   Cutty Sark |
| | 19. | Everest   Ganges   Po   Rhine   Nile   Thames   Tyne |
| | 20. | third   thrice   trio   zilch   triad |

Write each capital city and currency from the list next to its correct country.

Bangkok, Nicosia, Bolivar, Zloty, Warsaw, Baht, Pound, Moscow, Rouble, Caracas

| COUNTRY | CAPITAL | CURRENCY |
|---|---|---|
| 21. Russia | _____ | _____ |
| 22. Poland | _____ | _____ |
| 23. Thailand | _____ | _____ |
| 24. Cyprus | _____ | _____ |
| 25. Venezuela | _____ | _____ |

MARK
✓ or ✗

| | | | |
|---|---|---|---|
| Underline the ADVERBS in each of these sentences. | 26. | She came early and spoke first. | ☐ |
| | 27. | The thief ran fast down the path. | ☐ |
| | 28. | He looks well but is in some pain. | ☐ |
| | 29. | He is a very old man and walks slowly. | ☐ |
| | 30. | There is the spot where the horse fell heavily. | ☐ |

| | | | |
|---|---|---|---|
| Give two classifications (*proper* or *common* and *concrete* or *abstract*) for each of these nouns. | 31. | George     _____    _____ | ☐ |
| | 32. | fear     _____    _____ | ☐ |
| | 33. | wheelbarrow     _____    _____ | ☐ |
| | 34. | River Thames     _____    _____ | ☐ |
| | 35. | girl     _____    _____ | ☐ |

| | | | |
|---|---|---|---|
| Difficult spellings. Fill in the missing letters. | 36. | what you write on an envelope    a \_ \_ \_ \_ \_ \_ \_ | ☐ |
| | 37. | one's job or career    p \_ \_ \_ \_ \_ \_ \_ \_ \_ \_ | ☐ |
| | 38. | Words whose endings have the same sound do this.    r \_ \_ \_ \_ \_ | ☐ |
| | 39. | To achieve what you set out to do is to    s \_ \_ \_ \_ \_ \_ . | ☐ |
| | 40. | something that can be seen is    n \_ \_ \_ \_ \_ \_ \_ \_ \_ . | ☐ |

| | | | |
|---|---|---|---|
| Write the given foreign words and phrases next to their meanings. | | Deo volente,    raconteur,    non compos mentis,    début,    kamikaze | |
| | 41. | a storyteller _____ | ☐ |
| | 42. | self-destructive _____ | ☐ |
| | 43. | God willing _____ | ☐ |
| | 44. | insane _____ | ☐ |
| | 45. | one's first appearance _____ | ☐ |

| | | | |
|---|---|---|---|
| Here are some unusual names for colours. Write down the colour of which each one is a shade, e.g. rouge is a shade of red. | 46. | Ultramarine is a shade of _____ . | ☐ |
| | 47. | Beige is a shade of _____ . | ☐ |
| | 48. | Sable is a shade of _____ . | ☐ |
| | 49. | Scarlet is a shade of _____ . | ☐ |
| | 50. | Mauve is a shade of _____ . | ☐ |

| | | | |
|---|---|---|---|
| The prefix 'tri-' means 'three'. Complete these sentences. | 51. | A figure with three angles and three sides is a    tri \_ \_ \_ \_ \_ . | ☐ |
| | 52. | A sporting contest with three events is a    tri \_ \_ \_ \_ \_ \_ . | ☐ |
| | 53. | The French flag of three colours is known as the tri \_ \_ \_ \_ \_ \_ . | ☐ |
| | 54. | A pedal-powered vehicle with three wheels is a    tri \_ \_ \_ \_ \_ . | ☐ |
| | 55. | Neptune's three-pronged spear is a    tri \_ \_ \_ \_ \_ . | ☐ |

MARK
✓ or ✗

| | | |
|---|---|---|
| Put each of the given words into its correct sentence. | | enthusiast,  fanatic,  fan,  discussion,  argument |
| | 56. | Only a _____ would have a Union Jack tattooed on his forehead. |
| | 57. | John and I had a short _____ about our holiday plans. |
| | 58. | There was a fierce _____ about the cost of the scheme. |
| | 59. | The _____ would get up very carly to go fishing. |
| | 60. | The _____ followed the team wherever it went. |

| | | | |
|---|---|---|---|
| Form ADJECTIVES from these proper nouns. | 61. | Northumberland | the _____ pipes |
| | 62. | Cumbria | the _____ lakes and fells |
| | 63. | Belgium | the _____ capital of Brussels |
| | 64. | Malta | the _____ cross |
| | 65. | Argentina | the _____ cattle ranch |

| | | | |
|---|---|---|---|
| In each sentence write the past participle of the word in capitals. | 66. | CHIDE | She had _____ me for my carelessness. |
| | 67. | CLEAVE | With a mighty blow he had _____ the log in two. |
| | 68. | FORESEE | We could not have _____ what would happen. |
| | 69. | FORETELL | The prophet had _____ the future. |
| | 70. | STRIDE | He had angrily _____ up and down the driveway all morning waiting for the letter to arrive. |

| | | |
|---|---|---|
| Complete these definitions. | 71. | CARRION is a word meaning 'dead _____ '. |
| | 72. | If you CONFISCATE something you _____ . |
| | 73. | If you call somebody a NINCOMPOOP you mean that he or she is _____ . |
| | 74. | In a MUTINY, a ship's crew revolts against the _____ . |
| | 75. | PHARAOH was the title given to the kings of ancient _____ . |

| | | |
|---|---|---|
| Write down the authors of these well-known books. | 76. | The Adventures of Tom Sawyer _____ |
| | 77. | Black Beauty _____ |
| | 78. | The Canterbury Tales _____ |
| | 79. | The Wind in the Willows _____ |
| | 80. | The Witches, The BFG _____ |

MARK
✓ or ✗

Write each of the given popular phrases next to its meaning.

to sweep the board,  to curry favour,  to go the way of all flesh, like water off a duck's back,  touch-and-go

81. having no effect _____

82. to win everything _____

83. to try to win attention _____

84. to die _____

85. risky _____

In each sentence write a VERB formed from the word in capitals.

86. TYPE    She only buys clothes which _____ modern trends.

87. SALIVA    The starving man began to _____ when the aroma of the food assailed his nostrils.

88. HALF    The doctor told me I would have to _____ the amount of food I ate.

89. IDENTIFICATION    This is a security area and you must be able to _____ yourself.

90. NAUSEA    The gory sight _____ him.

Write down the antonyms of these words.

91. eastwards _____

92. vaguely _____

93. finite _____

94. heavily _____

95. adept _____

Join these pairs of sentences together. Your first word should be 'Having' and you should use a comma.

Example He ate his breakfast. He went to work.
becomes  Having eaten his breakfast, he went to work.

96. He put on his best suit. He walked to the church.

_____

97. She read the news in the 'Gazette'. She telephoned her mother.

_____

98. The burglar heard the alarm. He fled from the premises.

_____

99. He entered the office. He saw the book on the desk.

_____

100. The starving wolf saw the traveller. It attacked him at once.

_____

MARK
✓ or ✗

| | | |
|---|---|---|
| Rewrite correctly, putting in the necessary punctuation. | 1-5. | the play said george is the importance of being earnest by oscar wilde do you know it its very amusing <br><br> _____ <br> _____ <br> _____ |

Number between 0 and 5 ☐

| | | |
|---|---|---|
| Rewrite these sentences, changing masculines to feminines and vice versa. | 6. | The murderess of the mayor was the niece of a marquis. <br> _____ ☐ |
| | 7. | The wizard turned the prince into a stag. <br> _____ ☐ |
| | 8. | Her stallion chased the bachelor. <br> _____ ☐ |
| | 9. | Mr Brown is the grandson of his wife's masseuse. <br> _____ ☐ |
| | 10. | The executor of the will told the heir of his good fortune. <br> _____ ☐ |

| | | | | |
|---|---|---|---|---|
| Write down these pairs of homonyms. | 11. | water from the eyes _____ | rows above rows _____ | ☐ |
| | 12. | flat land _____ | joiner's tool _____ | ☐ |
| | 13. | a fruit _____ | it's vertical _____ | ☐ |
| | 14. | rains heavily _____ | holes in the skin _____ | ☐ |
| | 15. | let in water _____ | Welsh emblem _____ | ☐ |

| | | | |
|---|---|---|---|
| In each sentence write a NOUN formed from the word in capitals. | 16. | VARIOUS | I was amazed at the _____ of her interests. ☐ |
| | 17. | HATE | Cain was filled with _____ towards his brother. ☐ |
| | 18. | SERVE | Medieval peasants lived a life of _____ . ☐ |
| | 19. | MANLY | He was brave and strong, a figure of great _____ . ☐ |
| | 20. | DECEIVE | After his earlier _____ I could never bring myself to trust him again. ☐ |

| | | |
|---|---|---|
| Arrange these words alphabetically by writing the numbers 1-5 inside the brackets. | 21. | copper ( )   courage ( )   corn ( )   cooper ( )   cooling ( ) ☐ |
| | 22. | warrant ( )   warble ( )   warmth ( )   war ( )   warder ( ) ☐ |
| | 23. | German ( )   gerbil ( )   germ ( )   geriatric ( )   green ( ) ☐ |
| | 24. | pillion ( )   pill ( )   pillow ( )   pillory ( )   pilgrim ( ) ☐ |
| | 25. | vaguely ( )   vagrant ( )   vague ( )   vagary ( )   vagueness ( ) ☐ |

MARK
✓ or ✗

Write down the
meanings of these
'doubles'.

26.   rough-and-ready _____  ☐

27.   spick and span _____  ☐

28.   kith and kin _____  ☐

29.   all and sundry _____  ☐

30.   null and void _____  ☐

---

Write the missing
words from these
Latin or Greek roots.

31.   Aqua means water. A bridge carrying water is an _____ .  ☐

32.   Centum means a hundred. A hundred years is a _____ .  ☐

33.   Navis means ship. A fleet of ships is a _____ .  ☐

34.   Octo means eight. A creature with eight tentacles is
an _____ .

35.   Decimus means tenth. To kill every tenth person in a group is to
_____ that group.  ☐

---

Give two
classifications *(proper*
or *common* and
*concrete* or *abstract)*
for each of these
nouns.

36.   poet          _____        _____  ☐

37.   Mt. Etna     _____        _____  ☐

38.   hope          _____        _____  ☐

39.   love          _____        _____  ☐

40.   prig          _____        _____  ☐

---

Write each of the
given popular
phrases next to its
meaning.

teething troubles,  come hell or high water,  upset the apple-cart,
to force someone's hand,  get into deep water

41.   to make someone do something _____  ☐

42.   whatever it takes _____  ☐

43.   early problems _____  ☐

44.   spoil someone's plans _____  ☐

45.   get into serious trouble _____  ☐

---

Write down the
plurals of the words
in capitals.

46.   A CRISIS is an emergency and its plural is _____ .  ☐

47.   A CAMEO is a small role in a play and its plural is _____ .  ☐

48.   A CURIO is an article of bric-a-brac or anything thought to be rare
or curious. Its plural is _____ .  ☐

49.   A GLADIOLUS is a flower with sword-shaped leaves. Its plural can
be _____ or _____ .  ☐

50.   An APPENDIX is something added to a book. Its plural can be
either _____ or _____ .  ☐

| | | | | |
|---|---|---|---|---|
| In each sentence write an ADJECTIVE formed from the word in capitals. | 51. | LOGIC | There doesn't appear to be a _____ explanation. | ☐ |
| | 52. | INFORM | It was an _____ talk and I learned a lot from it. | ☐ |
| | 53. | DELIRIUM | She was _____ with joy when she heard the news. | ☐ |
| | 54. | DESPOT | The _____ ruler treated his subjects cruelly. | ☐ |
| | 55. | LOATHE | In the film a _____ monster emerged from the swamp with a dreadful shriek. | ☐ |

| | | | |
|---|---|---|---|
| Complete these proverbs. | 56. | Tell the truth and _____ | ☐ |
| | 57. | Many a true word _____ | ☐ |
| | 58. | Two wrongs _____ | ☐ |
| | 59. | One volunteer _____ | ☐ |
| | 60. | If you want a thing done well _____ | ☐ |

| | | | |
|---|---|---|---|
| Write down one word which describes all on each line. | 61. | teacher, lawyer, vicar, accountant _____ | ☐ |
| | 62. | Peter, Judas, Matthew, Thomas _____ | ☐ |
| | 63. | Oxford, Cambridge, Sorbonne, Yale _____ | ☐ |
| | 64. | Pavarotti, Caruso, Carreras, Domingo _____ | ☐ |
| | 65. | Capt. Kidd, Henry Morgan, Long John Silver _____ | ☐ |

| | | | |
|---|---|---|---|
| Supply the missing information. | 66. | A constellation is a _____ of _____ in the sky. | ☐ |
| | 67. | A newel post is found at _____ . | ☐ |
| | 68. | A filament is a very thin thread of wire inside a _____ . | ☐ |
| | 69. | Corpuscles are red or white _____ . | ☐ |
| | 70. | A spinnaker is a _____ on a _____ . | ☐ |

| | | | |
|---|---|---|---|
| Underline the odd one out. | 71. | elver   poult   hare   grilse   fry | ☐ |
| | 72. | copy   mimic   ape   imitate   cheat | ☐ |
| | 73. | Mohawk   Raven   Mohican   Sioux   Crow | ☐ |
| | 74. | Bible   Koran   Talmud   Thesaurus   Tantras | ☐ |
| | 75. | prudent   shrewd   canny   incautious   sagacious | ☐ |

| | | | |
|---|---|---|---|
| Work out these anagrams from the clues given. | 76. | NOT PAM H (a ghost) _____ | ☐ |
| | 77. | FLING IN BAR ZONE (a big fire – 2 words) _____ | ☐ |
| | 78. | ALANS ARMED (a lizard-like creature) _____ | ☐ |

MARK
✓ or ✗

| | | |
|---|---|---|
| Work out these anagrams from the clues given. | 79. | CRIED (something to drink) _____ | ☐ |
| | 80. | RED RUM (death) _____ | ☐ |

---

Put each of the given group terms in its correct sentence.

herd, building, bench, nest, pack, drove

81. A number of magistrates is called a _____ . ☐

82. A number of rabbits is called a _____ . ☐

83. A number of wolves is called a _____ . ☐

84. A number of cattle is called a _____ or a _____ . ☐

85. A number of rooks is called a _____ . ☐

---

Write each of the given words in its correct sentence.

veracity, voracity, loquacious, eloquent, reticent

86. That _____ child never seems to stop talking. ☐

87. We all admired her _____ and moving speech. ☐

88. We were sceptical and doubted the _____ of their story. ☐

89. The _____ child sat at the back and said nothing at all. ☐

90. The glutton was notorious for his _____ . ☐

---

Write down one word which has both the meanings given.

91. a mark with a meaning _____ to write one's signature ☐

92. a blood-sucking mite _____ the noise of a watch ☐

93. from waist to knees when sitting _____ to scoop up with the tongue ☐

94. sound made by a hound _____ an inlet of the sea ☐

95. machine for weaving _____ to appear out of the mist ☐

---

Put each of the given occupations into its correct sentence.

sexton, steeplejack, farrier, chandler, purser

96. The _____ began to repair the high church spire. ☐

97. The _____ put new shoes on my pony. ☐

98. The _____ tolled the bell when it was time for the service to begin. ☐

99. The _____ attended to the needs of the ship's passengers. ☐

100. A ship's _____ used to make candles but the word is now used to describe someone who sells equipment for boats and ships. ☐

MARK
✓ or ✗

| | | |
|---|---|---|
| Rewrite correctly, putting in all the necessary punctuation. | 1-5. | help cried the injured climber hoarsely im over here cant you see me |

_____

_____

_____

Number between 0 and 5 ☐

---

Put each of the given words into its correct sentence.

insomnia, myopia, dyspepsia, amnesia, dyslexia

6. After the road accident Kirsty suffered from _____ and could remember nothing of what had happened. ☐

7. _____ is word-blindness, causing many people great difficulty in learning to read and spell. ☐

8. People with _____ suffer from shortness of sight. ☐

9. _____ is painful digestion of one's food. ☐

10. Her _____ kept her awake for night after night. ☐

---

Give antonyms for these words.

11. midnight _____ ☐

12. sweet _____ ☐

13. juvenile _____ ☐

14. thrifty _____ ☐

15. permanent _____ ☐

---

Complete these analogies.

16. Swan Lake is to _____ as Aida is to opera. ☐

17. Henry is to eight as Elizabeth is to _____ . ☐

18. Nottingham was to lace as Sheffield was to _____ . ☐

19. David is to Goliath as Tortoise is to _____ . ☐

20. Birth is to death as _____ is to departure. ☐

---

Briefly explain these phrases.

21. layabout _____ ☐

22. lay into _____ ☐

23. layman/laywoman _____ ☐

24. lay-by _____ ☐

25. lay waste to _____ ☐

---

Write down the meanings of these abbreviations.

26. NOP _____ ☐

27. MC _____ ☐

28. IQ _____ ☐

29. ECU (or ecu) _____ ☐

30. BMX _____ ☐

MARK
✓ or ✗

| | | |
|---|---|---|
| Write down one word to describe all in each line. | 31. | arrow, bullet, torpedo, grenade _____ |
| | 32. | Victoria, Angel, Niagara, Reichenbach _____ |
| | 33. | Beaujolais, Bordeaux, Chianti, Riesling _____ |
| | 34. | zloty, rial, dinar, shekel _____ |
| | 35. | London, Vauxhall, Westminster, Tower _____ |

| | | |
|---|---|---|
| In each space write a NOUN formed from the word in capitals. | 36. | IMPETUOUS Because of his _____ he often made mistakes. |
| | 37. | LUXURIOUS The wealthy family lived a life of great _____ . |
| | 38. | OPAQUE Because of the _____ of the windscreen, we could not see where we were going. |
| | 39. | VULGAR We could not tolerate the _____ of their language. |
| | 40. | VIVACIOUS He was greatly charmed by her beauty and _____ . |

| | | |
|---|---|---|
| Underline the word which is closest in meaning to the one in capitals. | 41. | OCCIDENTAL   northern   eastern   western   southern   injurious |
| | 42. | HIRSUTE   stupid   costume   hairy   insipid   vague |
| | 43. | FACETIOUS   comfortable   ugly   smooth   witty   grand |
| | 44. | MARIONETTE   Mary   baby   carriage   dog   puppet |
| | 45. | SCULLION   beetle   servant   kitchen   watch   many |

| | | |
|---|---|---|
| Complete this information. | 46. | A tsunami is a huge _____ caused by an underwater earthquake. |
| | 47. | A hypochondriac always worries about his or her _____ . |
| | 48. | Maritime means bordering the _____ . |
| | 49. | Culinary is an adjective to do with _____ . |
| | 50. | A coroner enquires into the cause of death at an _____ . |

| | | |
|---|---|---|
| Underline the odd one out in each line. | 51. | Alberta   Dakota   Manitoba   Ontario   Saskatchewan |
| | 52. | Icknield   Eboracum   Fosse   Watling   Ermine |
| | 53. | loll   flop   loaf   slump   recession |
| | 54. | flavour   miasma   reek   smell   stench |
| | 55. | blubber   whinge   snivel   whimper   chortle |

MARK
✓ or ✗

| | | |
|---|---|---|
| The prefix 'mono-' means 'one' or 'single'. Complete these sentences. | 56. | Having only one husband or wife is   mono _ _ _ _ . |
| | 57. | A single eyeglass is called a   mono _ _ _ . |
| | 58. | A single sound which doesn't alter is a   mono _ _ _ _   and is   mono _ _ _ _ _ _ . |
| | 59. | Having all the power or all the property is a   mono _ _ _ _ . |
| | 60. | Something all the same colour is   mono _ _ _ _ _ _ . |

| | | |
|---|---|---|
| Complete these proverbs. | 61. | A watched pot _____ . |
| | 62. | Wilful waste _____ . |
| | 63. | He who hesitates _____ . |
| | 64. | All work and no play _____ . |
| | 65. | If a thing is worth doing _____ . |

| | | |
|---|---|---|
| Difficult spellings. Fill in the missing letters. | 66. | information and learning   k _ _ _ _ _ _ _ _ e |
| | 67. | on the roof, a television   a _ _ _ _ _ _ |
| | 68. | did well from something   b _ _ _ _ _ _ _ d |
| | 69. | a thin, crisp cake   b _ _ _ _ _ t |
| | 70. | one's employment or profession   b _ _ _ _ _ _ s |

| | | |
|---|---|---|
| Complete the similes, using the given words. | | life,   nails,   ice,   water,   new pin |
| | 71. | as cold as _____ |
| | 72. | as weak as _____ |
| | 73. | as large as _____ |
| | 74. | as neat as a _____ |
| | 75. | as hard as _____ |

| | | |
|---|---|---|
| Change the reported speech to direct speech. | 76. | Shabana remarked that she had not heard the postman come that morning. _____ _____ |
| | 77. | Linford asked the confectioner how much the cakes were. _____ _____ |
| | 78. | Everybody in the class was ordered by the teacher to stand up. _____ |
| | 79. | The mechanic shouted to his apprentice for some help. _____ |
| | 80. | The sergeant-major snarled at the cadets that they were a useless bunch of idiots. _____ _____ |

MARK
✓ or ✗

Write these five names in alphabetical order (the order in which they would appear in a telephone directory).

81.  R  Jackson  _____  ☐

82.  P  Jackson  _____  ☐

83.  A  Jacks  _____  ☐

84.  A  Jackson  _____  ☐

85.  T  L  James  _____  ☐

---

In these sentences change all masculines to feminines.

86.  Daniel and Nicholas ran to their stepfather.

_____  ☐

87.  Francis and Gerald were Scouts.

_____  ☐

88.  Victor and Michael paid their landlord the rent.

_____  ☐

89.  Andrew and Denis led the bullock to the field.

_____  ☐

90.  Henry was an abbot and Robert was a prior.

_____  ☐

---

Here are some unusual names for colours. Write down the colour of which each one is a shade, e.g. ruby is a shade of red.

91.  Cinnabar is a shade of _____ .  ☐

92.  Sepia is a shade of _____ .  ☐

93.  Lavender is a shade of _____ .  ☐

94.  Charcoal is a shade of _____ .  ☐

95.  Viridian is a shade of _____ .  ☐

---

Put each of these words into its correct sentence.

palate,  palette,  pallet,  paced,  paste

96.  The anxious student _____ up and down awaiting the result of her examination.  ☐

97.  The fine wine suited her _____ very well.  ☐

98.  I'm going to _____ the pictures in my scrap album.  ☐

99.  The ingots were stacked on a _____ waiting for the security firm to collect them.  ☐

100.  The artist mixed his colours on a _____ .  ☐

MARK
✓ or ✗

**Put one of the given words into each sentence.**

implement,   compliment,   complement,   competent

1.  The ship set sail with a full _____ of sailors on board.

2.  We must _____ the proposals which the council has made as soon as possible.

3.  A trowel is an _____ used by a builder.

4.  Are you sure this pilot is _____ enough to bring the ship into port?

5.  "I must _____ you," said the manager, "on the very high standard of workmanship you have displayed."

**Put each of the given foreign phrases next to its correct meaning.**

in memoriam,  faux pas,  modus operandi,  in situ,
pro tempore (pro tem)

6.  a blunder or mistake _____

7.  for the time being _____

8.  method of working or doing things _____

9.  in memory of _____

10. in place _____

**Difficult spellings. Write in the missing letters.**

11. discontented, not pleased   d _ _ _ _ _ _ _ _ _ _ d

12. clumsy or ungraceful   a _ _ _ _ _ d

13. to put something in place   i _ _ _ _ _ l

14. to vanish from sight   d _ _ _ _ _ _ _ r

15. likely to alter   c h _ _ _ _ _ _ _ _

**Write down one word in each of the blank spaces.**

16. A sleeplike state when one's mind can respond to the command of another person is called _____ .

17. The art of speaking so as to give the illusion that the sound comes from somewhere else is known as _____ .

18. One who is recovering health after an illness or an operation is called a _____ .

19. The adjective 'geriatric' refers to people who are _____ . They are looked after by a doctor called a _____ .

20. A judge who decides between parties in a dispute is called an _____ .

**Underline the VERBS in these sentences.**

21. They laughed and giggled as they ran all the way home.

22. The angry postman bit the dog.

23. I arrived twenty minutes late for the appointment.

MARK
✓ or ✗

| | | |
|---|---|---|
| Underline the VERBS in these sentences. | 24. | Mansoor said he was going to watch the match. |
| | 25. | ''Come here!'' she shouted as Daniel ran away. |

| | | |
|---|---|---|
| Here are some unusual names for colours. Write down the colour of which each one is a shade. | 26. | Cobalt is a shade of _____ . |
| | 27. | Burgundy is a shade of _____ . |
| | 28. | Jade is a shade of _____ . |
| | 29. | Ivory is a shade of _____ . |
| | 30. | Jonquil is a shade of _____ . |

| | | |
|---|---|---|
| Give two classifications (proper or common and concrete or abstract) for each of these nouns. | 31. | rodent _____ _____ |
| | 32. | Brer Rabbit _____ _____ |
| | 33. | Robin _____ _____ |
| | 34. | robin _____ _____ |
| | 35. | hate _____ _____ |

| | | |
|---|---|---|
| In each sentence write an ADVERB formed from the word in capitals. | 36. | BIGAMY    John Smith was arrested after _____ marrying a second woman. |
| | 37. | HUNGER    At break-time she _____ ate the sandwich. |
| | 38. | BRUTE    The dog was treated _____ by its owner. |
| | 39. | ENIGMA    He smiled _____ but said nothing. |
| | 40. | EERIE    Sarah's voice echoed _____ in the empty house. |

| | | |
|---|---|---|
| Complete the group terms, using the given words. | | wool,   raspberries,   cats,   snipe,   lions |
| | 41. | a punnet of _____ |
| | 42. | a skein of _____ |
| | 43. | a pride of _____ |
| | 44. | a wisp of _____ |
| | 45. | a clowder of _____ |

| | | |
|---|---|---|
| Write down the antonyms of these words. | 46. | summery _____ |
| | 47. | wrongful _____ |
| | 48. | sickness _____ |
| | 49. | knowledge _____ |
| | 50. | smallness _____ |

MARK
✓ or ✗

| | | | |
|---|---|---|---|
| In each sentence write a NOUN formed from the word in capitals. | 51. | PERSPIRE | After a gruelling race, _____ dripped from my body. |
| | 52. | FRAGRANT | A wonderful _____ came from the herb garden. |
| | 53. | DROWSY | As I lay in the warm sunlight, a feeling of _____ stole over me. |
| | 54. | ALERT | Thanks to the watchman's _____ the fire was spotted in time. |
| | 55. | HARASS | "I don't need all this _____," said John. |

| | | |
|---|---|---|
| The prefix 'oct-' or 'octo-' means 'eight'. Complete these sentences. | 56. | A figure with eight sides and angles is an   oct _ _ _ _ . |
| | 57. | A group of eight musicians is an   oct _ _ . |
| | 58. | The eighth month in the Roman calendar was   Oct _ _ _ _ . |
| | 59. | The eight hundredth anniversary of an event is its octo _ _ _ _ _ _ _ _ . |
| | 60. | A set of eight is an   oct _ _ _ . |

| | | |
|---|---|---|
| Fill in the missing words in these sentences. | 61. | The large kettledrums in an orchestra are known as _____ . |
| | 62. | A word meaning 'of the sun' is   s_____ . |
| | 63. | A word meaning 'like a fox' is   v_____ . |
| | 64. | A fish from which the bones have been removed is a   _____ . |
| | 65. | Guilty or innocent? The jury arrives at its _____ . |

| | | |
|---|---|---|
| Underline the correct word in the brackets. | 66. | A person who sells hats is a  (milliner,  draper,  hosier). |
| | 67. | A place where animals are slaughtered is an (apiary,  abattoir,  abacus). |
| | 68. | A clergyman speaks from a  (soapbox,  pulpit,  rostrum). |
| | 69. | A person who builds in stone is a  (builder,  sculptor,  mason). |
| | 70. | To swing to and fro like a pendulum is to (oscillate,  obfuscate,  capitulate). |

| | | | |
|---|---|---|---|
| In each sentence write an ADJECTIVE formed from the word in capitals. | 71. | MOURN | The soprano sang a very _____ song. |
| | 72. | DECIDE | We won a _____ victory in the match last Saturday. |
| | 73. | GLOBE | Scientists warn us of the dangers of _____ warming. |
| | 74. | TALK | The _____ boy was asked to be a little quieter. |
| | 75. | NERVE | I felt very _____ going through the forest. |

MARₑ
✓ or ✗

**Rewrite these sentences, putting in the necessary punctuation.**

76.  this cup a beautiful piece of work belongs to me

_____  ☐

77.  every day at about this time the postman calls

_____  ☐

78.  having seen his enemy approaching the knight ran to face him

_____  ☐

79.  this event more than any other has given us hope

_____  ☐

80.  noticing that the door was ajar the constable entered the room

_____  ☐

**Briefly describe these phrases.**

81.  Adam's ale _____  ☐
82.  Adam's apple _____  ☐
83.  apple-pie order _____  ☐
84.  apple-pie bed _____  ☐
85.  apple of one's eye _____  ☐

**These are the first lines of some famous poems. Write down the name of each poet.**

86.  Hamelin Town's in Brunswick, _____  ☐
87.  My love is like a red, red rose, _____  ☐
88.  Tiger! Tiger! burning bright, _____  ☐
89.  I wandered lonely as a cloud, _____  ☐
90.  Three jolly farmers Once bet a pound _____  ☐

**Complete these analogies.**

91.  Cavalry is to ride as _____ is to march.  ☐
92.  Words are to libretto as _____ is to score.  ☐
93.  Negative is to no as _____ is to yes.  ☐
94.  Ambrosia is to _____ as food is to drink.  ☐
95.  Philatelist is to stamps as _____ is to coins.  ☐

**Fill in the missing information.**

96.  Another word for THESPIAN is _____ .  ☐
97.  VERBIAGE means a lot of _____ .  ☐
98.  A DIVA is _____ .  ☐
99.  MAINTENANCE is _____ paid to a spouse after a

_____ .  ☐

100. If something is GRATIS, it costs _____ .  ☐

44

44444

**MARK**
✓ or ✗

**Complete these proverbs.**

1. Every dog _____ .
2. Cleanliness _____ .
3. Don't cross the bridge _____ .
4. Let bygones _____ .
5. Beggars cannot _____ .

**Put apostrophes where necessary in these sentences.**

6. Bobs book isnt on Mr Williamss desk.
7. Youre about to find out what its like to do a decent days work.
8. Hell come round at three oclock on Shabanas bicycle.
9. The babies clothes were taken to the childrens nursery by Mums pal.
10. Ones entitled to know whether this purse is yours or hers.

**On each line write one word which has both the meanings given.**

11. to go round _____ a woman's garment
12. fixed _____ a business
13. imposing and majestic _____ a month of the year
14. a flat-bottomed boat _____ the Irish pound
15. used to span a river _____ a card game

**In which sports are these trophies played for?**

16. Lonsdale Belt _____
17. America's Cup _____
18. The Ashes _____
19. Davis Cup _____
20. FA Cup _____

**Write each of the given foreign phrases next to its correct meaning.**

joie de vivre, bon voyage, siesta, billet-doux, exempli gratia (e.g.)

21. have a good trip _____
22. for example _____
23. a love-letter _____
24. an afternoon nap _____
25. enjoyment of life _____

**Difficult spellings. Fill in the missing letters.**

26. time to enjoy yourself   l _ _ _ _ _ _
27. the right use of language   g _ _ _ _ _ _ _
28. keeping something in working order   m _ _ _ _ _ _ _ _ c e
29. an account of what something is like   d _ _ _ _ _ _ _ _ _
30. to say something is good or suitable   r _ _ _ _ _ _ _ _

ENGLISH PROGRESS PAPER 24 · PAGE 1    45

MARK
✓ or ✗

**Complete the similes using the given words.**

mouse, pikestaff, clockwork, bone, ditchwater

31. as regular as _____

32. as dull as _____

33. as dry as a _____

34. as plain as a _____

35. as timid as a _____

**Here are some more unusual names for colours. Write down the colour of which each one is a shade, e.g. violet is a shade of purple.**

36. Azure is a shade of _____.

37. Carmine is a shade of _____.

38. Dun is a shade of _____.

39. Eggshell is a shade of _____.

40. Eau-de-Nil is a shade of _____.

**Write the correct capital city and currency from the list next to each of these countries.**

Wellington, Guilder, Schilling, Birr, Dollar, The Hague, Krona, Vienna, Addis Ababa, Reykjavik

| COUNTRY | CAPITAL | CURRENCY |
|---|---|---|
| 41. Iceland | _____ | _____ |
| 42. New Zealand | _____ | _____ |
| 43. Netherlands | _____ | _____ |
| 44. Austria | _____ | _____ |
| 45. Ethiopia | _____ | _____ |

**Put each of the given words into its correct sentence.**

braise, braze, brays, born, borne

46. He had _____ the heavy burden for a great distance.

47. I was able to _____ the two pieces of metal together.

48. If you _____ the steak it will make it tender.

49. The donkey _____ each morning and wakes me up.

50. William Shakespeare was _____ in 1564 and died in 1616.

**Write down the missing parts of speech of the words in capitals.**

| NOUN | ADJECTIVE | ADVERB | VERB |
|---|---|---|---|
| 51. _____ | _____ | _____ | REPEAT |
| 52. _____ | VILE | _____ | |
| 53. _____ | _____ | _____ | DERIDE |
| 54. _____ | SIMPLE | _____ | |
| 55. NATION | _____ | _____ | |

MARK
✓ or ✗

| | | |
|---|---|---|
| Put each of the given ADJECTIVES into its correct sentence. | | pristine, ineffectual, fickle, perspicacious, sterling |
| | 56. | "It was extremely _____ of you," said Professor Sullivan, "to solve that problem so quickly and efficiently." |
| | 57. | Bill's _____ qualities made him an ideal candidate for such a responsible post. |
| | 58. | Lucy's _____ use of the boat's oars rendered her incapable of rowing across the fast-flowing river. |
| | 59. | Seamus has collected model cars for many years, but only those which are in _____ condition. |
| | 60. | I never cease to be amazed by the _____ moods of the English climate. |

| | | |
|---|---|---|
| The prefix 'quad-' means 'four'. Complete these sentences. | 61. | A figure with four sides is a   quad _ _ _ _ _ _ _ _ _ . |
| | 62. | A creature with four legs is a   quad _ _ _ _ _ . |
| | 63. | If you multiply a number by four you   quad _ _ _ _ _   it. |
| | 64. | Four babies born at the same time to the same mother are called quad _ _ _ _ _ _ s. |
| | 65. | The fourth part of a circle is called a   quad _ _ _ _ . |

| | | | |
|---|---|---|---|
| In each sentence write a VERB formed from the word in capitals. | 66. | VEXATION | "Don't _____ me any more," said Mother crossly. |
| | 67. | PORTENT | "What does this sign _____ ?" he asked. |
| | 68. | BATH | It is said that Queen Elizabeth I would _____ only once a year. |
| | 69. | CIRCLE | We were ordered to _____ the enemy before we attacked. |
| | 70. | COMPANY | Charlotte asked her brother to _____ her to the bus stop. |

| | | |
|---|---|---|
| Supply the missing information. | 71. | A large floating mass of ice in the sea is an _____ . |
| | 72. | The apparatus which shows on a screen any approaching ships or aircraft is called _____ . |
| | 73. | The chief (or bishop's) church in a diocese is known as the _____ . |
| | 74. | "Richard of York gave battle in vain" is a way of remembering the colours of the rainbow . It is a   mn_____ . |
| | 75. | Spaghetti, macaroni and lasagne are kinds of _____ . |

| | | |
|---|---|---|
| Briefly describe these expressions. | 76. | blue blood _____ |
| | 77. | blue-collar _____ |

MARK
✓ or ✗

Briefly describe these expressions.

78. blue stocking _____ ☐

79. blue-eyed boy _____ ☐

80. blueprint _____ ☐

---

In each sentence write a NOUN formed from the word in capitals.

81. TURBULENT    Because of severe _____ the aircraft was forced to descend to a lower altitude. ☐

82. MONOTONOUS    Andrew found the _____ of the job depressing. ☐

83. RECKLESS    The sheer _____ of his driving was bound to cause an accident sooner or later. ☐

84. INCOMPETENT    Karen's _____ gained her the sack. ☐

85. HAPPY    The children's faces beamed with _____ when Santa entered the room. ☐

---

Write down one word to describe all in each line.

86. Amundsen, Cook, Drake, Magellan, Shackleton _____ ☐

87. butler, cook, footman, maid, valet _____ ☐

88. fly, bantam, feather, middle, heavy _____ ☐

89. Kennedy, Reagan, Carter, Clinton _____ ☐

90. merino, Soay, Cheviot, Wensleydale _____ ☐

---

In each line underline the odd one out.

91. Nigeria   Chad   Bolivia   Ethiopia   Mozambique ☐

92. generous   bountiful   liberal   parsimonious   unstinting ☐

93. bishop   priest   layman   cardinal   pope ☐

94. procrastinate   expedite   dally   prolong   retard ☐

95. twilight   dawn   dusk   gloaming   sundown ☐

---

Put each of the given words into its correct sentence.

prologue, monologue, dialogue, epilogue, synagogue

96. A _____ is a place of worship for Jewish people. ☐

97. A _____ is a conversation between two or more people. ☐

98. A _____ is an introduction to a poem or a play. ☐

99. A _____ is a speech for just one person. ☐

100. An _____ is the end part of a book or play or the conclusion of a radio or television programme. ☐